Jamila at the fair

Tessa Krailing

Nelson

Jamila saw a poster in the Square.
It said a fair was coming.
'Have you been to a fair?' asked Ben.
'No,' said Jamila.
'We will take you,' said Rocky and Ben.

3

There were swings and roundabouts and
dodgem cars.
Jamila looked at all the rides.
'I don't know what to do first,' she said.
'Let's go on the dodgems,' said Ben.

Ben bumped into Jamila's car.
Jamila bumped into Rocky's car, and
Rocky bumped into all the other cars.

Next they went on a roundabout.
Jamila rode on a white horse.
The music played and the roundabout
went around.
'It is like flying!' said Jamila.

'Let's go on the ghost train next,' said Ben.
The train went into a dark tunnel.
When a ghost jumped out, Jamila and Ben
screamed.
'That ghost did not frighten me,' said Rocky.
'I'm much too brave to be frightened by a stupid
ghost.'

Rocky began to stand up.
'Sit down, Rocky,' shouted Ben.
'Don't be stupid!'

Suddenly a big hand came out from the wall,
hitting Rocky.
'Don't let the monsters hit me again!'
screamed Rocky.
Rocky did not look brave now – he looked white!

'Were you afraid in there?' asked Jamila.
But when she looked around, Rocky and
Ben were not there.
Where were they?

'Roll up, roll up!' said the man.
'Be quick for the next ride.'
'Please, did you see my friends?' asked Jamila.
'No one here,' said the man, and went back to
shouting, 'Roll up, roll up!'

Jamila went away.
She went to look for Rocky and Ben.
'Jamila, we are here!' shouted Rocky.
'We were playing a joke on you!'

Jamila was too far away and
she did not hear Rocky shout.

'Come here, little girl,'
said the fortune teller,
'and I will tell your fortune.'
'No, no,' said Jamila.
'I must look for my friends.'

Jamila saw a little dog.
It was white with dark marks on its feet.
The dog was playing with a thin stick.
'Hello, little dog,' said Jamila,
taking the stick from the dog.
'Do you want to play?'

'Here, dog – go and get the stick,' said Jamila.
The little dog ran after the stick.
It picked up the stick and took it back to Jamila.

'I can't play with you all day,' said Jamila.
'I have to find Rocky and Ben.'
'Rocky! Ben!' she called. 'Where are you?'
The little dog followed Jamila through the fair.

Jamila found a policeman.
'This dog has followed me,' she said.
'I don't know where he lives.
What shall I do with him?'

The policeman took Jamila and the dog
to see the man from the RSPCA.
'I've found this dog,' said Jamila.
'Do you know if one is missing?'

19

The RSPCA man looked at the dog.
He looked at the marks on its feet.
'I think I know who owns this dog,' he said.

The fortune teller was pleased to see her dog.
'He's always going off to play on his own,' she said.
She tied the dog to her poster stand.

MADAM
ROSE

FORTUNE
TELLER

21

Just then Rocky and Ben came over.
'We've been looking all over for you,' they said.
'What do you want to do next?'
'I've saved my money for two rides on
the roundabout,' said Jamila.

'My friend owns the roundabout,'
said the fortune teller.
'I will tell him to let you have
all the rides that you want.'

Jamila, Ben and Rocky went on
the roundabout again.
Jamila had lots of rides on her favourite white horse.
She was pleased that she had come to the fair.